Robert Louis Stevenson (13 November 1850 – 3 December 1894) was a Scottish novelist and travel writer, most noted for Treasure Island, Kidnapped, Strange Case of Dr Jekyll and Mr Hyde, and A Child's Garden of Verses. Born and educated in Edinburgh, Stevenson suffered from serious bronchial trouble for much of his life, but continued to write prolifically and travel widely, in defiance of his poor health. As a young man, he mixed in London literary circles, receiving encouragement from Andrew Lang, Edmund Gosse, Leslie Stephen and W. E. Henley, the last of whom may have provided the model for Long John Silver in Treasure Island. His travels took him to France, America and Australia, before he finally settled in Samoa, where he died. A celebrity in his lifetime, Stevenson attracted a more negative critical response for much of the 20th century, though his reputation has been largely restored. He is currently ranked as the 26th most translated author in the world.(Source: Wikipedia)

Literary works:

The Hair Trunk or The Ideal Commonwealth (1877)
Unfinished and unpublished.
Treasure Island (1883)
Prince Otto (1885)
Strange Case of Dr Jekyll and Mr Hyde (1886),
Kidnapped (1886)
The Black Arrow: A Tale of the Two Roses (1888)
The Master of Ballantrae: A Winter's Tale (1889),
The Wrong Box (1889)
The Wrecker (1892); co-written with Lloyd Osbourne.
Catriona (1893)
The Ebb-Tide (1894); co-written with Lloyd Osbourne.
Weir of Hermiston (1896)

THRONE CLASSICS

The Sea Fogs & The Waif Woman

Robert Louis Stevenson

This is a work of fiction. Names, characters, places, and incidents either are the product of the author's imagination or are used fictitiously. Any resemblance to actual persons, living or dead, events, or locales is entirely coincidental.

First Printing: 2020

ISBN 978-93-90171-34-7 (paperback)

ISBN 978-93-90171-35-4 (Hardcover)

Published by Throne Classics

www.throneclassics.com

Contents

The Sea Fogs
&
The Waif Woman

THE SEA FOGS

A sheeted spectre white and tall,

The cold mist climbs the castle wall

And lays its hand upon thy cheek.

—Longfellow.

INTRODUCTION

Robert Louis Stevenson first came to California in 1879 for the purpose of getting married. The things that delayed his marriage are sufficiently set forth in his "Letters" (edited by Sidney Colvin) and in his "Life" (written by Graham Balfour). It is here necessary to refer only to the last of the obstacles, the breaking down of his health. It is in connection with the evil thing that came to him at this time that he first makes mention of "the sea fogs," that beset a large part of the California coast. He speaks of them as poisonous; and poisonous they are to any one who is afflicted with pulmonary weakness, but bracing and glorious to others. They give the charm of climate to dwellers around the great bay. How he took this first very serious attack of the terrible malady is indicated in the letter to Edmund Gosse, dated April 16, 1880. His attitude toward death is shown here, and is further shown in his little paper AEs Triplex, in which he successfully vindicates his generation from the charge of cowardice in the face of death. Stevenson's two distinguishing characteristics were his courage and his determination to be happy as the right way of making other people happy. His courage, far more than change of scene and climate, gave him fourteen more years in which to contribute to the sweetness and light of the world. These years were made fruitful to others by his determined happiness, a happiness in which the main factor, outside of his own determination, came from the companionship which his marriage brought to him. The great principles by which he lived influenced those who did not know him personally, through his gift of writing. He always maintained that it was not a gift but an achievement, and that any one could write as well as he by taking as much pains. We may well doubt the soundness of this theory, but we cannot doubt the spiritual attitude from which it came. It came from no mock humility, but from a feeling that nothing was creditable to him except what he did. He asked no credit for the talents committed to his charge. He asked credit only for the use be made of the talents.

Stevenson was married May 19, 1880. His health, which had delayed the marriage, determined the character of the honeymoon. He must get away from the coast and its fogs. His honeymoon experiences are recorded in one of the most delightful of his minor writings, "The Silverado Squatters." He went, with his wife, his stepson and a dog, to squat on the eastern shoulder of Mount Saint Helena, a noble mountain which closes and dominates the Napa Valley, a wonderful and fertile valley, running northward from the bay of San Francisco. Silverado was a deserted mining-camp. Stevenson has intimated that there are more ruined cities in California than in the land of Bashan, and in one of these he took up his residence for about two months, "camping" in the deserted quarters of the extinct mining company. Had he gone a little beyond the toll-house, just over the shoulder of the mountain, he would probably never have seen the glory of "the sea fogs." It would have been better for his health but worse for English literature.

My first knowledge of that glory came to me twenty years ago. I had come to California to care for one dearly beloved by me, who was fighting the same fight that Stevenson fought, and against the same enemy, and who was fighting it just as bravely. I took him to the summit of the Santa Cruz Mountains in the hope that we might escape the fogs. As I watched on the porch of the little cottage where he lay, I saw night after night what I believe to be the most beautiful of all natural phenomena, the sea fog of the Pacific, seen from above. Under the full moon, or under the early sun which slowly withers it away, the great silver sea with its dark islands of redwood seemed to me the most wonderful of things. With my wonder and delight, perhaps making them more poignant, was the fear lest the glory should mount too high, and lay its attractive hand on my beloved. The fog has been dear to me ever since. I have often grumbled at it when I was in it or under it, but when I have seen it from above, that first thrill of wonder and delight has come back to me —always. Whether on the Berkeley hills I see its irresistible columns moving through the Golden Gate across the bay to take possession of the land, or whether I stand on the height of Tamalpais and look at the white, tangled flood below,—

"My heart leaps up when I behold."

It remains to me—

"A vision, a delight and a desire."

When the beauty of the fog first got hold of me, I wondered whether any one had given literary expression to its supreme charm. I searched the works of some of the better-known California poets, not quite without result. I was familiar with what seem to me the best of the serious verses of Bret Harte, the lines on San Francisco,—wherein the city is pictured as a penitent Magdalen, cowled in the grey of the Franciscans, —the soft pale grey of the sea fog. The literary value of the figure is hardly injured by the cold fog that the penitence of this particular Magdalen has never been of an enduring quality. It is to be noted that what Harte speaks of is not the beauty of the fog, but its sobriety and dignity.

Sill, with his susceptibility to the infinite variety of nature and with the spark of the divine fire which burned in him, refers often to some of the effects of the fog, such as the wonderful sunset colors on the Berkeley hills in summer. But I find only one direct allusion to the beauty of the fog itself:—

(1)"There lies a little city in the hills;

White are its roofs, dim is each dwelling's door,

And peace with perfect rest its bosom fills.

"There the pure mist, the pity of the sea,

Comes as a white, soft hand, and reaches o'er

And touches its still face most tenderly."

In 1887 I had not read "The Silverado Squatters." Part of it had been published in Scribner's Magazine. It was only in the following year that I got hold of the book and found an almost adequate expression of my own feeling about the sea fogs. Stevenson did not know all their beauty, for he was not here long enough, but he could tell what he saw. In other words, he had a gift which is denied to most of us.

Silverado is now a quite impossible place for squatting. When I first tried to enter, I found it so given over to poison-oak and rattlesnakes that I did not care to pursue my investigations very far. I did not know at that time that I was quite immune from the poison of the oak and that the California rattlesnake was quite so friendly and harmless an animal as John Muir has since assured us that he is. The last time that I passed Silverado, it was accessible only by the aid of a gang of wood-choppers.

Curiously, the last great fog effect that I have seen was almost the same which Stevenson has described. Last summer we had been staying for a month with our friends who have a summer home about three miles beyond Stevenson's "toll-house." It is, I believe, the most beautiful country-seat on this round earth, and its free and gentle hospitality cannot be surpassed. We left this delightful place of sojourning between three and four o'clock in the morning to catch the early train from Calistoga. Our steep climb up to the toll-house was under the broad smile of the moon, which gradually gave way to the brilliant dawn. When we passed the toll-house, the whole Napa Valley should have been revealed to us, but it was not. The fog had surged through it and had hidden it. What we saw was better than the beautiful Napa Valley. I should like to tell what we saw, but I cannot,—"For what can the man do who cometh after the king?"

(1) This exquisite little poem is unaccountably omitted from the Household (and presumably complete) Edition of Sill's poems issued by Houghton, Mifflin & Co., 1906. It is found in the little volume, "Poems," by Edward Rowland Sill, published by the same firm at an earlier date. Mountain View Cemetery is no longer a "little city."

THE SEA FOGS

A change in the colour of the light usually called me in the morning. By a certain hour, the long, vertical chinks in our western gable, where the boards had shrunk and separated, flashed suddenly into my eyes as stripes of dazzling blue, at once so dark and splendid that I used to marvel how the qualities could be combined. At an earlier hour, the heavens in that quarter were still quietly coloured, but the shoulder of the mountain which shuts in the canyon already glowed with sunlight in a wonderful compound of gold and rose and green; and this too would kindle, although more mildly and with rainbow tints, the fissures of our crazy gable. If I were sleeping heavily, it was the bold blue that struck me awake; if more lightly, then I would come to myself in that earlier and fairer light.

One Sunday morning, about five, the first brightness called me. I rose and turned to the east, not for my devotions, but for air. The night had been very still. The little private gale that blew every evening in our canyon, for ten minutes or perhaps a quarter of an hour, had swiftly blown itself out; in the hours that followed, not a sigh of wind had shaken the treetops; and our barrack, for all its breaches, was less fresh that morning than of wont. But I had no sooner reached the window than I forgot all else in the sight that met my eyes, and I made but two bounds into my clothes, and down the crazy plank to the platform.

The sun was still concealed below the opposite hilltops, though it was shining already, not twenty feet above my head, on our own mountain slope. But the scene, beyond a few near features, was entirely changed. Napa Valley was gone; gone were all the lower slopes and woody foothills of the range; and in their place, not a thousand feet below me, rolled a great level ocean. It was as though I had gone to bed the night before, safe in a nook of inland mountains and had awakened in a bay upon the coast. I had seen these inundations from below; at Calistoga I had risen and gone abroad in the early morning, coughing and sneezing, under fathoms on fathoms of gray sea vapour, like a cloudy sky—a dull sight for the artist, and a painful experience for the invalid. But to sit aloft one's self in the pure air and under the unclouded dome of heaven, and thus look down on the submergence of the valley, was strangely different and even delightful to the eyes. Far away were hilltops like little islands. Nearer, a smoky surf beat about the foot of precipices and poured into all the coves of these rough mountains. The colour of that fog ocean was a thing never to be forgotten. For an instant, among the Hebrides and just about sundown, I have seen something like it on the sea itself. But the white was not so opaline; nor was there, what surprisingly increased the effect, that breathless crystal stillness over all. Even in its gentlest moods the salt sea travails, moaning among the weeds or lisping on the sand; but that vast fog ocean lay in a trance of silence, nor did the sweet air of the morning tremble with a sound.

As I continued to sit upon the dump, I began to observe that this sea was not so level as at first sight it appeared to be. Away in the extreme south, a little hill of fog arose against the sky above the general surface, and as it had already caught the sun it shone on the horizon like the topsails of some giant ship. There were huge waves, stationary, as it seemed, like waves in a frozen sea; and yet, as I looked again, I was not sure but they were moving after all, with a slow and august advance. And while I was yet doubting, a promontory of the hills some four or five miles away, conspicuous by a bouquet of tall pines, was in a single instant overtaken and swallowed up. It reappeared in a little, with its pines, but this time as an islet and only to be swallowed up once more and then for good. This set me looking nearer, and I saw that in every cove along the line of mountains the fog was being piled in higher and higher, as though by some wind that was inaudible to me. I could trace its progress, one pine tree first growing hazy and then disappearing after another; although sometimes there was none of this forerunning haze, but the whole opaque white ocean gave a start and swallowed a piece of mountain at a gulp. It was to flee these poisonous fogs that I had left the seaboard, and climbed so high among the mountains. And now, behold, here came the fog to besiege me in my chosen altitudes, and yet came so beautifully that my first thought was of welcome.

The sun had now gotten much higher, and through all the gaps of the hills it cast long bars of gold across that white ocean. An eagle, or some other very great bird of the mountain, came wheeling over the nearer pinetops, and hung, poised and something sideways, as if to look abroad on that unwonted desolation, spying, perhaps with terror, for the eyries of her comrades. Then, with a long cry, she disappeared again toward Lake County and the clearer air. At length it seemed to me as if the flood were beginning to subside. The old landmarks, by whose disappearance I had measured its advance, here a crag, there a brave pine tree, now began, in the inverse order, to make their reappearance into daylight. I judged all danger of the fog was over. This was not Noah's flood; it was but a morning spring, and would now drift out seaward whence it came. So, mightily relieved, and a good deal exhilarated by the sight, I went into the house to light the fire.

I suppose it was nearly seven when I once more mounted the platform to look abroad. The fog ocean had swelled up enormously since last I saw it; and a few hundred feet below me, in the deep gap where the Toll House stands and the road runs through into Lake County, it had already topped the slope, and was pouring over and down the other side like driving smoke. The wind had climbed along with it; and though I was still in calm air, I could see the trees tossing below me, and their long, strident sighing mounted to me where I stood.

Half an hour later, the fog had surmounted all the ridge on the opposite side of the gap, though a shoulder of the mountain still warded it out of our canyon. Napa Valley and its bounding hills were now utterly blotted out. The fog, sunny white in the sunshine, was pouring over into Lake County in a huge, ragged cataract, tossing treetops appearing and disappearing in the spray. The air struck with a little chill, and set me coughing. It smelt strong of the fog, like the smell of a washing-house, but with a shrewd tang of the sea-salt.

Had it not been for two things—the sheltering spur which answered as a dyke, and the great valley on the other side which rapidly engulfed whatever mounted—our own little platform in the canyon must have been already buried a hundred feet in salt and poisonous air. As it was, the interest of the scene entirely occupied our minds. We were set just out of the wind, and but just above the fog; we could listen to the voice of the one as to music on the stage; we could plunge our eyes down into the other, as into some flowing stream from over the parapet of a bridge; thus we looked on upon a strange, impetuous, silent, shifting exhibition of the powers of nature, and saw the familiar landscape changing from moment to moment like figures in a dream.

The imagination loves to trifle with what is not. Had this been indeed the deluge, I should have felt more strongly, but the emotion would have been similar in kind. I played with the idea as the child flees in delighted terror from the creations of his fancy. The look of the thing helped me. And when at last I began to flee up the mountain, it was indeed partly to escape from the raw air that kept me coughing, but it was also part in play.

As I ascended the mountainside, I came once more to overlook the upper surface of the fog; but it wore a different appearance from what I had beheld at daybreak. For, first, the sun now fell on it from high overhead, and its surface shone and undulated like a great nor'land moor country, sheeted with untrodden morning snow. And, next, the new level must have been a thousand or fifteen hundred feet higher than the old, so that only five or six points of all the broken country below me still stood out. Napa Valley was now one with Sonoma on the west. On the hither side, only a thin scattered fringe of bluffs was unsubmerged; and through all the gaps the fog was pouring over, like an ocean into the blue clear sunny country on the east. There it was soon lost; for it fell instantly into the bottom of the valleys, following the watershed; and the hilltops in that quarter were still clear cut upon the eastern sky.

Through the Toll House gap and over the near ridges on the other side, the deluge was immense. A spray of thin vapour was thrown high above it, rising and falling, and blown into fantastic shapes. The speed of its course was like a mountain torrent. Here and there a few treetops were discovered and then whelmed again; and for one second, the bough of a dead pine beckoned out of the spray like the arm of a drowning man. But still the imagination was dissatisfied, still the ear waited for something more. Had this indeed been water (as it seemed so, to the eye), with what a plunge of reverberating thunder would it have rolled upon its course, disembowelling mountains and deracinating pines And yet water it was and sea-water at that—true Pacific billows, only somewhat rarefied, rolling in mid-air among the hilltops.

I climbed still higher, among the red rattling gravel and dwarf underwood of Mount Saint Helena, until I could look right down upon Silverado, and admire the favoured nook in which it lay. The sunny plain of fog was several hundred feet higher; behind the protecting spur a gigantic accumulation of cottony vapour threatened, with every second to blow over and submerge our homestead; but the vortex setting past the Toll House was too strong; and there lay our little platform, in the arms of the deluge, but still enjoying its unbroken sunshine. About eleven, however, thin spray came flying over the friendly buttress, and I began to think the fog had hunted out its Jonah after all. But it was the last effort. The wind veered while we were at dinner, and began to blow squally from the mountain summit and by half-past one all that world of sea fogs was utterly routed and flying here and there into the south in little rags of cloud. And instead of a lone sea-beach, we found ourselves once more inhabiting a high mountainside, with the clear green country far below us, and the light smoke of Calistoga blowing in the air.

This was the great Russian campaign for that season. Now and then, in the early morning, a little white lakelet of fog would be seen far down in Napa Valley but the heights were not again assailed, nor was the surrounding world again shut off from Silverado.

THE WAIF WOMAN

A CUE—FROM A SAGA

This is a tale of Iceland, the isle of stories, and of a thing that befell in the year of the coming there of Christianity.

In the spring of that year a ship sailed from the South Isles to traffic, and fell becalmed inside Snowfellness. The winds had speeded her; she was the first comer of the year; and the fishers drew alongside to hear the news of the south, and eager folk put out in boats to see the merchandise and make prices. From the doors of the hall on Frodis Water, the house folk saw the ship becalmed and the boats about her, coming and going; and the merchants from the ship could see the smoke go up and the men and women trooping to their meals in the hall.

The goodman of that house was called Finnward Keelfarer, and his wife Aud the Light-Minded; and they had a son Eyolf, a likely boy, and a daughter Asdis, a slip of a maid. Finnward was well-to-do in his affairs, he kept open house and had good friends. But Aud his wife was not so much considered: her mind was set on trifles, on bright clothing, and the admiration of men, and the envy of women; and it was thought she was not always so circumspect in her bearing as she might have been, but nothing to hurt.

On the evening of the second day men came to the house from sea. They told of the merchandise in the ship, which was well enough and to be had at easy rates, and of a waif woman that sailed in her, no one could tell why, and had chests of clothes beyond comparison, fine coloured stuffs, finely woven, the best that ever came into that island, and gewgaws for a queen. At the hearing of that Aud's eyes began to glisten. She went early to bed; and the day was not yet red before she was on the beach, had a boat launched, and was pulling to the ship. By the way she looked closely at all boats, but there was no woman in any; and at that she was better pleased, for she had no fear of the men.

When they came to the ship, boats were there already, and the merchants and the shore folk sat and jested and chaffered in the stern. But in the fore part of the ship, the woman sat alone, and looked before her sourly at the sea. They called her Thorgunna. She was as tall as a man and high in flesh, a buxom wife to look at. Her hair was of the dark red, time had not changed it. Her face was dark, the cheeks full, and the brow smooth. Some of the merchants told that she was sixty years of age and others laughed and said she was but forty; but they spoke of her in whispers, for they seemed to think that she was ill to deal with and not more than ordinary canny.

Aud went to where she sat and made her welcome to Iceland. Thorgunna did the honours of the ship. So for a while they carried it on, praising and watching each other, in the way of women. But Aud was a little vessel to contain a great longing, and presently the cry of her heart came out of her.

"The folk say," says she, "you have the finest women's things that ever came to Iceland?" and as she spoke her eyes grew big.

"It would be strange if I had not," quoth Thorgunna. "Queens have no finer."

So Aud begged that she might see them.

Thorgunna looked on her askance. "Truly," said she, "the things are for no use but to be shown." So she fetched a chest and opened it. Here was a cloak of the rare scarlet laid upon with silver, beautiful beyond belief; hard by was a silver brooch of basket work that was wrought as fine as any shell and was as broad as the face of the full moon; and Aud saw the clothes lying folded in the chest, of all the colours of the day, and fire, and precious gems; and her heart burned with envy. So, because she had so huge a mind to buy, she began to make light of the merchandise.

"They are good enough things," says she, "though I have better in my chest at home. It is a good enough cloak, and I am in need of a new cloak." At that she fingered the scarlet, and the touch of the fine stuff went to her mind like singing. "Come," says she, "if it were only for your civility in showing it, what will you have for your cloak?"

"Woman," said Thorgunna, "I am no merchant." And she closed the chest and locked it, like one angry.

Then Aud fell to protesting and caressing her. That was Aud's practice; for she thought if she hugged and kissed a person none could say her nay. Next she went to flattery, said she knew the things were too noble for the like of her—they were made for a stately, beautiful woman like Thorgunna; and at that she kissed her again, and Thorgunna seemed a little pleased. And now Aud pled poverty and begged for the cloak in a gift; and now she vaunted the wealth of her goodman and offered ounces and ounces of fine silver, the price of three men's lives. Thorgunna smiled, but it was a grim smile, and still she shook her head. At last Aud wrought herself into extremity and wept.

"I would give my soul for it," she cried.

"Fool!" said Thorgunna. "But there have been fools before you!" And a little after, she said this: "Let us be done with beseeching. The things are mine. I was a fool to show you them; but where is their use, unless we show them? Mine they are and mine they shall be till I die. I have paid for them dear enough," said she.

Aud saw it was of no avail; so she dried her tears, and asked Thorgunna about her voyage, and made believe to listen while she plotted in her little mind. "Thorgunna," she asked presently, "do you count kin with any folk in Iceland?"

"I count kin with none," replied Thorgunna. "My kin is of the greatest, but I have not been always lucky, so I say the less."

"So that you have no house to pass the time in till the ship return?" cries Aud. "Dear Thorgunna, you must come and live with us. My goodman is rich, his hand and his house are open, and I will cherish you like a daughter."

At that Thorgunna smiled on the one side; but her soul laughed within her at the woman's shallowness. "I will pay her for that word daughter," she thought, and she smiled again.

"I will live with you gladly," says she, "for your house has a good name, and I have seen the smoke of your kitchen from the ship. But one thing you shall understand. I make no presents, I give nothing where I go—not a rag and not an ounce. Where I stay, I work for my upkeep; and as I am strong as a man and hardy as an ox, they that have had the keeping of me were the better pleased."

It was a hard job for Aud to keep her countenance, for she was like to have wept. And yet she felt it would be unseemly to eat her invitation; and like a shallow woman and one that had always led her husband by the nose, she told herself she would find some means to cajole Thorgunna and come by her purpose after all. So she put a good face on the thing, had Thorgunna into the boat, her and her two great chests, and brought her home with her to the hall by the beach.

All the way in she made much of the wife; and when they were arrived gave her a locked bed-place in the hall, where was a bed, a table, and a stool, and space for the two chests.

"This shall be yours while you stay here," said Aud. And she attended on her guest.

Now Thorgunna opened the second chest and took out her bedding—sheets of English linen, the like of it never seen, a cover of quilted silk, and curtains of purple wrought with silver. At the sight of these Aud was like one distracted, greed blinded her mind; the cry rose strong in her throat, it must out.

"What will you sell your bedding for?" she cried, and her cheeks were hot.

Thorgunna looked upon her with a dusky countenance. "Truly you are a courteous hostess," said she, "but I will not sleep on straw for your amusement."

At that Aud's two ears grew hot as her cheeks; and she took Thorgunna at her word; and left her from that time in peace.

The woman was as good as her spoken word. Inside the house and out she wrought like three, and all that she put her hand to was well done. When she milked, the cows yielded beyond custom; when she made hay, it was always dry weather; when she took her turn at the cooking, the folk licked their spoons. Her manners when she pleased were outside imitation, like one that had sat with kings in their high buildings. It seemed she was pious too, and the day never passed but she was in the church there praying. The rest was not so well. She was of few words, and never one about her kin and fortunes. Gloom sat on her brow, and she was ill to cross. Behind her back they gave her the name of the Waif Woman or the Wind Wife; to her face it must always be Thorgunna. And if any of the young men called her mother, she would speak no more that day, but sit apart in the hall and mutter with her lips.

"This is a queer piece of goods that we have gotten," says Finnward Keelfarer, "I wish we get no harm by her! But the good wife's pleasure must be done," said he, which was his common word.

When she was at work, Thorgunna wore the rudest of plain clothes, though ever clean as a cat; but at night in the hall she was more dainty, for she loved to be admired. No doubt she made herself look well, and many thought she was a comely woman still, and to those she was always favourable and full of pleasant speech. But the more that some pleased her, it was thought by good judges that they pleased Aud the less.

When midsummer was past, a company of young men upon a journey came to the house by Frodis Water. That was always a great day for Aud, when there were gallants at table; and what made this day the greater, Alf of the Fells was in the company, and she thought Alf fancied her. So be sure Aud wore her best. But when Thorgunna came from the bed-place, she was arrayed like any queen and the broad brooch was in her bosom. All night in the hall these women strove with each other; and the little maid, Asdis, looked on, and was ashamed and knew not why. But Thorgunna pleased beyond all; she told of strange things that had befallen in the world; when she pleased she had the cue to laughter; she sang, and her voice was full and her songs new in that island; and whenever she turned, the eyes shone in her face and the brooch glittered at her bosom. So that the young men forgot the word of the merchants as to the woman's age, and their looks followed her all night.

Aud was sick with envy. Sleep fled her; her husband slept, but she sat upright beside him in the bed, and gnawed her fingers. Now she began to hate Thorgunna, and the glittering of the great brooch stood before her in the dark. "Sure," she thought, "it must be the glamour of that brooch! She is not so fair as I; she is as old as the dead in the hillside; and as for her wit and her songs, it is little I think of them!" Up she got at that, took a light from the embers, and came to her guest's bed-place. The door was locked, but Aud had a master-key and could go in. Inside, the chests were open, and in the top of one the light of her taper shone upon the glittering of the brooch. As a dog snatches food she snatched it, and turned to the bed. Thorgunna lay on her side; it was to be thought she slept, but she talked the while to herself, and her lips moved. It seemed her years returned to her in slumber, for her face was grey and her brow knotted; and the open eyes of her stared in the eyes of Aud. The heart of the foolish woman died in her bosom; but her greed was the stronger, and she fled with that which she had stolen.

When she was back in bed, the word of Thorgunna came to her mind, that these things were for no use but to be shown. Here she had the brooch and the shame of it, and might not wear it. So all night she quaked with the fear of discovery, and wept tears of rage that she should have sinned in vain. Day came, and Aud must rise; but she went about the house like a crazy woman. She saw the eyes of Asdis rest on her strangely, and at that she beat the maid. She scolded the house folk, and, by her way of it, nothing was done aright. First she was loving to her husband and made much of him, thinking to be on his good side when trouble came. Then she took a better way, picked a feud with him, and railed on the poor man till his ears rang, so that he might be in the wrong beforehand. The brooch she hid without, in the side of a hayrick. All this while Thorgunna lay in the bed-place, which was not her way, for by custom she was early astir. At last she came forth, and there was that in her face that made all the house look one at the other and the heart of Aud to be straitened. Never a word the guest spoke, not a bite she swallowed, and they saw the strong shudderings take and shake her in her place. Yet a little, and still without speech, back she went into her bad-place, and the door was shut.

"That is a sick wife," said Finnward, "Her weird has come on her."

And at that the heart of Aud was lifted up with hope.

All day Thorgunna lay on her bed, and the next day sent for Finnward.

"Finnward Keelfarer," said she, "my trouble is come upon me, and I am at the end of my days."

He made the customary talk.

"I have had my good things; now my hour is come; and let suffice," quoth she. "I did not send for you to hear your prating."

Finnward knew not what to answer, for he saw her soul was dark.

"I sent for you on needful matters," she began again. "I die here—I!—in this black house, in a bleak island, far from all decency and proper ways of man; and now my treasure must be left. Small pleasure have I had of it, and leave it with the less!" cried she.

"Good woman, as the saying is, needs must," says Finnward, for he was nettled with that speech.

"For that I called you," quoth Thorgunna. "In these two chests are much wealth and things greatly to be desired. I wish my body to be laid in Skalaholt in the new church, where I trust to hear the mass-priests singing over my head so long as time endures. To that church I will you to give what is sufficient, leaving your conscience judge of it. My scarlet cloak with the silver, I will to that poor fool your wife. She longed for it so bitterly, I may not even now deny her. Give her the brooch as well. I warn you of her; I was such as she, only wiser; I warn you, the ground she stands upon is water, and whoso trusts her leans on rottenness. I hate her and I pity her. When she comes to lie where I lie—" There she broke off. "The rest of my goods I leave to your black-eyed maid, young Asdis, for her slim body and clean mind. Only the things of my bed, you shall see burned."

"It is well," said Finnward.

"It may be well," quoth she, "if you obey. My life has been a wonder to all and a fear to many. While I lived none thwarted me and prospered. See to it that none thwart me after I am dead. It stands upon your safety."

"It stands upon my honour," quoth Finnward, "and I have the name of an honourable man."

"You have the name of a weak one," says Thorgunna. "Look to it, look to it, Finnward. Your house shall rue it else."

"The rooftree of my house is my word," said Finnward.

"And that is a true saying," says the woman. "See to it, then. The speech of Thorgunna is ended."

With that she turned her face against the wall and Finnward left her.

The same night, in the small hours of the clock, Thorgunna passed. It was a wild night for summer, and the wind sang about the eaves and clouds covered the moon, when the dark woman wended. From that day to this no man has learned her story or her people's name; but be sure the one was stormy and the other great. She had come to that isle, a waif woman, on a ship; thence she flitted, and no more remained of her but her heavy chests and her big body.

In the morning the house women streaked and dressed the corpse. Then came Finnward, and carried the sheets and curtains from the house, and caused build a fire upon the sands. But Aud had an eye on her man's doings.

"And what is this that you are at?" said she.

So he told her.

"Burn the good sheets!" she cried. "And where would I be with my two hands? No, troth," said Aud, "not so long as your wife is above ground!"

"Good wife," said Finnward, "this is beyond your province. Here is my word pledged and the woman dead I pledged it to. So much the more am I bound. Let me be doing as I must, goodwife."

"Tilly-valley!" says she, "and a fiddlestick's end, goodman! You may know well about fishing and be good at shearing sheep for what I know; but you are little of a judge of damask sheets. And the best word I can say is just this," she says, laying hold of one end of the goods, "that if ye are made up to burn the plenishing, you must burn your wife along with it."

"I trust it will not go so hard," says Finnward, "and I beg you not to speak so loud and let the house folk hear you."

"Let them speak low that are ashamed!" cries Aud. "I speak only in reason."

"You are to consider that the woman died in my house," says Finnward, "and this was her last behest. In truth, goodwife, if I were to fail, it is a thing that would stick long in my throat, and would give us an ill name with the neighbours."

"And you are to consider," says she, "that I am your true wife and worth all the witches ever burnt, and loving her old husband"—here she put her arms about his neck. "And you are to consider that what you wish to do is to destroy fine stuff, such as we have no means of replacing; and that she bade you do it singly to spite me, for I sought to buy this bedding from her while she was alive at her own price; and that she hated me because I was young and handsome."

"That is a true word that she hated you, for she said so herself before she wended," says Finnward.

"So that here is an old faggot that hated me, and she dead as a bucket," says Aud; "and here is a young wife that loves you dear, and is alive forby"—and at that she kissed him—"and the point is, which are you to do the will of?"

The man's weakness caught him hard, and he faltered. "I fear some hurt will come of it," said he.

There she cut in, and bade the lads tread out the fire, and the lasses roll the bed-stuff up and carry it within.

"My dear," says he, "my honour—this is against my honour."

But she took his arm under hers, and caressed his hand, and kissed his knuckles, and led him down the bay. "Bubble-bubble-bubble!" says she, imitating him like a baby, though she was none so young. "Bubble-bubble, and a silly old man! We must bury the troll wife, and here is trouble enough, and a vengeance! Horses will sweat for it before she comes to Skalaholt; 'tis my belief she was a man in a woman's habit. And so now, have done, good man, and let us get her waked and buried, which is more than she deserves, or her old duds are like to pay for. And when that is ended, we can consult upon the rest."

So Finnward was but too well pleased to put it off.

The next day they set forth early for Skalaholt across the heaths. It was heavy weather, and grey overhead; the horses sweated and neighed, and the men went silent, for it was nowhere in their minds that the dead wife was canny. Only Aud talked by the way, like a silly sea-gull piping on a cliff, and the rest held their peace. The sun went down before they were across Whitewater; and the black night fell on them this side of Netherness. At Netherness they beat upon the door. The goodman was not abed nor any of his folk, but sat in the hall talking; and to them Finnward made clear his business.

"I will never deny you a roof," said the goodman of Netherness. "But I have no food ready, and if you cannot be doing without meat, you must e'en fare farther."

They laid the body in a shed, made fast their horses, and came into the house, and the door was closed again. So there they sat about the lights, and there was little said, for they were none so well pleased with their reception. Presently, in the place where the food was kept, began a clattering of dishes; and it fell to a bondman of the house to go and see what made the clatter. He was no sooner gone than he was back again; and told it was a big, buxom woman, high in flesh and naked as she was born, setting meats upon a dresser. Finnward grew pale as the dawn; he got to his feet, and the rest rose with him, and all the party of the funeral came to the buttery-door. And the dead Thorgunna took no heed of their coming, but went on setting forth meats, and seemed to talk with herself as she did so; and she was naked to the buff.

Great fear fell upon them; the marrow of their back grew cold. Not one word they spoke, neither good nor bad; but back into the hall, and down upon their bended knees, and to their prayers.

"Now, in the name of God, what ails you?" cried the goodman of Netherness.

And when they had told him, shame fell upon him for his churlishness.

"The dead wife reproves me," said the honest man.

And he blessed himself and his house, and caused spread the tables, and they all ate of the meats that the dead wife laid out.

This was the first walking of Thorgunna, and it is thought by good judges it would have been the last as well, if men had been more wise.

The next day they came to Skalaholt, and there was the body buried, and the next after they set out for home. Finnward's heart was heavy, and his mind divided. He feared the dead wife and the living; he feared dishonour and he feared dispeace; and his will was like a sea-gull in the wind. Now he cleared his throat and made as if to speak; and at that Aud cocked her eye and looked at the goodman mocking, and his voice died unborn. At the last, shame gave him courage.

"Aud," said he, "yon was a most uncanny thing at Netherness."

"No doubt," said Aud.

"I have never had it in my mind," said he, "that yon woman was the thing she should be."

"I dare say not," said Aud. "I never thought so either."

"It stands beyond question she was more than canny," says Finnward, shaking his head. "No manner of doubt but what she was ancient of mind."

"She was getting pretty old in body, too," says Aud.

"Wife," says he, "it comes in upon me strongly this is no kind of woman to disobey; above all, being dead and her walking. I think, wife, we must even do as she commanded."

"Now what is ever your word?" says she, riding up close and setting her hand upon his shoulder. "'The goodwife's pleasure must be done'; is not that my Finnward?"

"The good God knows I grudge you nothing," cried Finnward. "But my blood runs cold upon this business. Worse will come of it!" he cried, "worse will flow from it!"

"What is this todo?" cries Aud. "Here is an old brimstone hag that should have been stoned with stones, and hated me besides. Vainly she tried to frighten me when she was living; shall she frighten me now when she is dead and rotten? I trow not. Think shame to your beard, goodman! Are these a man's shoes I see you shaking in, when your wife rides by your bridle-hand, as bold as nails?"

"Ay, ay," quoth Finnward. "But there goes a byword in the country: Little wit, little fear."

At this Aud began to be concerned, for he was usually easier to lead. So now she tried the other method on the man.

"Is that your word?" cried she. "I kiss the hands of ye! If I have not wit enough, I can rid you of my company. Wit is it he seeks?" she cried. "The old broomstick that we buried yesterday had wit for you."

So she rode on ahead and looked not the road that he was on.

Poor Finnward followed on his horse, but the light of the day was gone out, for his wife was like his life to him. He went six miles and was true to his heart; but the seventh was not half through when he rode up to her.

"Is it to be the goodwife's pleasure?" she asked.

"Aud, you shall have your way," says he; "God grant there come no ill of it!"

So she made much of him, and his heart was comforted.

When they came to the house, Aud had the two chests to her own bed-place, and gloated all night on what she found. Finnward looked on, and trouble darkened his mind.

"Wife," says he at last, "you will not forget these things belong to Asdis?"

At that she barked upon him like a dog.

"Am I a thief?" she cried. "The brat shall have them in her turn when she grows up. Would you have me give her them now to turn her minx's head with?"

So the weak man went his way out of the house in sorrow and fell to his affairs. Those that wrought with him that day observed that now he would labour and toil like a man furious, and now would sit and stare like one stupid; for in truth he judged the business would end ill.

For a while there was no more done and no more said. Aud cherished her treasures by herself, and none was the wiser except Finnward. Only the cloak she sometimes wore, for that was hers by the will of the dead wife; but the others she let lie, because she knew she had them foully, and she feared Finnward somewhat and Thorgunna much.

At last husband and wife were bound to bed one night, and he was the first stripped and got in. "What sheets are these?" he screamed, as his legs touched them, for these were smooth as water, but the sheets of Iceland were like sacking.

"Clean sheets, I suppose," says Aud, but her hand quavered as she wound her hair.

"Woman!" cried Finnward, "these are the bed-sheets of Thorgunna—these are the sheets she died in! do not lie to me!"

At that Aud turned and looked at him. "Well?" says she, "they have been washed."

Finnward lay down again in the bed between Thorgunna's sheets, and groaned; never a word more he said, for now he knew he was a coward and a man dishonoured. Presently his wife came beside him, and they lay still, but neither slept.

It might be twelve in the night when Aud felt Finnward shudder so strong that the bed shook.

"What ails you?" said she.

"I know not," he said. "It is a chill like the chill of death. My soul is sick with it." His voice fell low. "It was so Thorgunna sickened," said he. And he arose and walked in the hall in the dark till it came morning.

Early in the morning he went forth to the sea-fishing with four lads. Aud was troubled at heart and watched him from the door, and even as he went down the beach she saw him shaken with Thorgunna's shudder. It was a rough day, the sea was wild, the boat laboured exceedingly, and it may be that Finnward's mind was troubled with his sickness. Certain it is that they struck, and their boat was burst, upon a skerry under Snowfellness. The four lads were spilled into the sea, and the sea broke and buried them, but Finnward was cast upon the skerry, and clambered up, and sat there all day long: God knows his thoughts. The sun was half-way down, when a shepherd went by on the cliffs about his business, and spied a man in the midst of the breach of the loud seas, upon a pinnacle of reef. He hailed him, and the man turned and hailed again. There was in that cove so great a clashing of the seas and so shrill a cry of sea-fowl that the herd might hear the voice and nor the words. But the name Thorgunna came to him, and he saw the face of Finnward Keelfarer like the face of an old man. Lively ran the herd to Finnward's house; and when his tale was told there, Eyolf the boy was lively to out a boat and hasten to his father's aid. By the strength of hands they drove the keel against the seas, and with skill and courage Eyolf won upon the skerry and climbed up, There sat his father dead; and this was the first vengeance of Thorgunna against broken faith.

It was a sore job to get the corpse on board, and a sorer yet to bring it home before the rolling seas. But the lad Eyolf was a lad of promise, and the lads that pulled for him were sturdy men. So the break-faith's body was got home, and waked, and buried on the hill. Aud was a good widow and wept much, for she liked Finnward well enough. Yet a bird sang in her ears that now she might marry a young man. Little fear that she might have her choice of them, she thought, with all Thorgunna's fine things; and her heart was cheered.

Now, when the corpse was laid in the hill, Asdis came where Aud sat solitary in hall, and stood by her awhile without speech.

"Well, child?" says Aud; and again "Well?" and then "Keep us holy, if you have anything to say, out with it!"

So the maid came so much nearer, "Mother," says she, "I wish you would not wear these things that were Thorgunna's."

"Aha," cries Aud. "This is what it is? You begin early, brat! And who has been poisoning your mind? Your fool of a father, I suppose." And then she stopped and went all scarlet. "Who told you they were yours?" she asked again, taking it all the higher for her stumble. "When you are grown, then you shall have your share and not a day before. These things are not for babies."

The child looked at her and was amazed. "I do not wish them," she said. "I wish they might be burned."

"Upon my word, what next?" cried Aud. "And why should they be burned?"

"I know my father tried to burn these things," said Asdis, "and he named Thorgunna's name upon the skerry ere he died. And, O mother, I doubt they have brought ill luck."

But the more Aud was terrified, the more she would make light of it.

Then the girl put her hand upon her mother's. "I fear they are ill come by," said she.

The blood sprang in Aud's face. "And who made you a judge upon your mother that bore you?" cried she.

"Kinswoman," said Asdis, looking down, "I saw you with the brooch."

"What do you mean? When? Where did you see me?" cried the mother.

"Here in the hall," said Asdis, looking on the floor, "the night you stole it."

At that Aud let out a cry. Then she heaved up her hand to strike the child. "You little spy!" she cried. Then she covered her face, and wept, and rocked herself. "What can you know?" she cried. "How can you understand, that are a baby, not so long weaned? He could—your father could, the dear good man, dead and gone! He could understand and pity, he was good to me. Now he has left me alone with heartless children! Asdis," she cried, "have you no nature in your blood? You do not know what I have done and suffered for them. I have done—oh, and I could have done anything! And there is your father dead. And after all, you ask me not to use them? No woman in Iceland has the like. And you wish me to destroy them? Not if the dead should rise!" she cried. "No, no," and she stopped her ears, "not if the dead should rise, and let that end it!"

So she ran into her bed-place, and clapped at the door, and left the child amazed.

But for all Aud spoke with so much passion, it was noticed that for long she left the things unused. Only she would be locked somewhile daily in her bed-place, where she pored on them and secretly wore them for her pleasure.

Now winter was at hand; the days grew short and the nights long; and under the golden face of morning the isle would stand silver with frost. Word came from Holyfell to Frodis Water of a company of young men upon a journey; that night they supped at Holyfell, the next it would be at Frodis Water; and Alf of the Fells was there, and Thongbrand Ketilson, and Hall the Fair. Aud went early to her bed-place, and there she pored upon these fineries till her heart was melted with self-love. There was a kirtle of a mingled colour, and the blue shot into the green, and the green lightened from the blue, as the colours play in the ocean between deeps and shallows: she thought she could endure to live no longer and not wear it. There was a bracelet of an ell long, wrought like a serpent and with fiery jewels for the eyes; she saw it shine on her white arm and her head grew dizzy with desire. "Ah!" she thought, "never were fine lendings better met with a fair wearer." And she closed her eyelids, and she thought she saw herself among the company and the men's eyes go after her admiring. With that she considered that she must soon marry one of them and wondered which; and she thought Alf was perhaps the best, or Hall the Fair, but was not certain, and then she remembered Finnward Keelfarer in his cairn upon the hill, and was concerned. "Well, he was a good husband to me," she thought, "and I was a good wife to him. But that is an old song now." So she turned again to handling the stuffs and jewels. At last she got to bed in the smooth sheets, and lay, and fancied how she would look, and admired herself, and saw others admire her, and told herself stories, till her heart grew warm and she chuckled to herself between the sheets. So she shook awhile with laughter; and then the mirth abated but not the shaking; and a grue took hold upon her flesh, and the cold of the grave upon her belly, and the terror of death upon her soul. With that a voice was in her ear: "It was so Thorgunna sickened." Thrice in the night the chill and the terror took her, and thrice it passed away; and when she rose on the morrow, death had breathed upon her countenance.

She saw the house folk and her children gaze upon her; well she knew why! She knew her day was come, and the last of her days, and her last hour was at her back; and it was so in her soul that she scarce minded. All was lost, all was past mending, she would carry on until she fell. So she went as usual, and hurried the feast for the young men, and railed upon her house folk, but her feet stumbled, and her voice was strange in her own ears, and the eyes of the folk fled before her. At times, too, the chill took her and the fear along with it; and she must sit down, and the teeth beat together in her head, and the stool tottered on the floor. At these times, she thought she was passing, and the voice of Thorgunna sounded in her ear: "The things are for no use but to be shown," it said. "Aud, Aud, have you shown them once? No, not once!"

And at the sting of the thought her courage and strength would revive, and she would rise again and move about her business.

Now the hour drew near, and Aud went to her bed-place, and did on the bravest of her finery, and came forth to greet her guests. Was never woman in Iceland robed as she was. The words of greeting were yet between her lips, when the shuddering fell upon her strong as labour, and a horror as deep as hell. Her face was changed amidst her finery, and the faces of her guests were changed as they beheld her: fear puckered their brows, fear drew back their feet; and she took her doom from the looks of them, and fled to her bed-place. There she flung herself on the wife's coverlet, and turned her face against the wall.

That was the end of all the words of Aud; and in the small hours on the clock her spirit wended. Asdis had come to and fro, seeing if she might help, where was no help possible of man or woman. It was light in the bed-place when the maid returned, for a taper stood upon a chest. There lay Aud in her fine clothes, and there by her side on the bed the big dead wife Thorgunna squatted on her hams. No sound was heard, but it seemed by the movement of her mouth as if Thorgunna sang, and she waved her arms as if to singing.

"God be good to us!" cried Asdis, "she is dead."

"Dead," said the dead wife.

"Is the weird passed?" cried Asdis.

"When the sin is done the weird is dreed," said Thorgunna, and with that she was not.

But the next day Eyolf and Asdis caused build a fire on the shore betwixt tide-marks. There they burned the bed-clothes, and the clothes, and the jewels, and the very boards of the waif woman's chests; and when the tide returned it washed away their ashes. So the weird of Thorgunna was lifted from the house on Frodis Water.

About Author

Childhood and youth

Stevenson was born at 8 Howard Place, Edinburgh, Scotland on 13 November 1850 to Thomas Stevenson (1818–87), a leading lighthouse engineer, and his wife Margaret Isabella (born Balfour, 1829–97). He was christened Robert Lewis Balfour Stevenson. At about age 18, he changed the spelling of "Lewis" to "Louis", and he dropped "Balfour" in 1873.

Lighthouse design was the family's profession; Thomas's father (Robert's grandfather) was civil engineer Robert Stevenson, and Thomas's brothers (Robert's uncles) Alan and David were in the same field. Thomas's maternal grandfather Thomas Smith had been in the same profession. However, Robert's mother's family were gentry, tracing their lineage back to Alexander Balfour who had held the lands of Inchyra in Fife in the fifteenth century. His mother's father Lewis Balfour (1777–1860) was a minister of the Church of Scotland at nearby Colinton, and her siblings included physician George William Balfour and marine engineer James Balfour. Stevenson spent the greater part of his boyhood holidays in his maternal grandfather's house. "Now I often wonder what I inherited from this old minister," Stevenson wrote. "I must suppose, indeed, that he was fond of preaching sermons, and so am I, though I never heard it maintained that either of us loved to hear them."

Lewis Balfour and his daughter both had weak chests, so they often needed to stay in warmer climates for their health. Stevenson inherited a tendency to coughs and fevers, exacerbated when the family moved to a damp, chilly house at 1 Inverleith Terrace in 1851. The family moved again to the sunnier 17 Heriot Row when Stevenson was six years old, but the tendency to extreme sickness in winter remained with him until he was 11. Illness was a recurrent feature of his adult life and left him extraordinarily thin. Contemporaneous views were that he had tuberculosis, but more recent views are that it was bronchiectasis or even sarcoidosis.

Stevenson's parents were both devout Presbyterians, but the household was not strict in its adherence to Calvinist principles. His nurse Alison Cunningham (known as Cummy) was more fervently religious. Her mix of Calvinism and folk beliefs were an early source of nightmares for the child, and he showed a precocious concern for religion. But she also cared for him tenderly in illness, reading to him from John Bunyan and the Bible as he lay sick in bed and telling tales of the Covenanters. Stevenson recalled this time of sickness in "The Land of Counterpane" in A Child's Garden of Verses (1885), dedicating the book to his nurse.

Stevenson was an only child, both strange-looking and eccentric, and he found it hard to fit in when he was sent to a nearby school at age 6, a problem repeated at age 11 when he went on to the Edinburgh Academy; but he mixed well in lively games with his cousins in summer holidays at Colinton. His frequent illnesses often kept him away from his first school, so he was taught for long stretches by private tutors. He was a late reader, learning at age 7 or 8, but even before this he dictated stories to his mother and nurse, and he compulsively wrote stories throughout his childhood. His father was proud of this interest; he had also written stories in his spare time until his own father found them and told him to "give up such nonsense and mind your business." He paid for the printing of Robert's first publication at 16, entitled The Pentland Rising: A Page of History, 1666. It was an account of the Covenanters' rebellion which was published in 1866, the 200th anniversary of the event.

Education

In September 1857, Stevenson went to Mr Henderson's School in India Street, Edinburgh, but because of poor health stayed only a few weeks and did not return until October 1859. During his many absences he was taught by private tutors. In October 1861, he went to Edinburgh Academy, an independent school for boys, and stayed there sporadically for about fifteen months. In the autumn of 1863, he spent one term at an English boarding school at Spring Grove in Isleworth in Middlesex (now an urban area of West London). In October 1864, following an improvement to his health, he was sent to Robert Thomson's private school in Frederick Street, Edinburgh, where he remained until he went to university. In November 1867, Stevenson entered the University of Edinburgh to study engineering. He showed from the start no enthusiasm for his studies and devoted much energy to avoiding lectures. This time was more important for the friendships he made with other students in the Speculative Society (an exclusive debating club), particularly with Charles Baxter, who would become Stevenson's financial agent, and with a professor, Fleeming Jenkin, whose house staged amateur drama in which Stevenson took part, and whose biography he would later write. Perhaps most important at this point in his life was a cousin, Robert Alan Mowbray Stevenson (known as "Bob"), a lively and light-hearted young man who, instead of the family profession, had chosen to study art. Each year during vacations, Stevenson travelled to inspect the family's engineering works—to Anstruther and Wick in 1868, with his father on his official tour of Orkney and Shetland islands lighthouses in 1869, and for three weeks to the island of Erraid in 1870. He enjoyed the travels more for the material they gave for his writing than for any engineering interest. The voyage with his father pleased him because a similar journey of Walter Scott with Robert Stevenson had provided the inspiration for Scott's 1822 novel The Pirate. In April 1871, Stevenson notified his father of his decision to pursue a life of letters. Though the elder Stevenson was naturally disappointed, the surprise cannot have been great, and Stevenson's mother reported that he was "wonderfully resigned" to his son's choice. To provide some security, it was agreed that Stevenson should read Law (again at Edinburgh University) and be called to the Scottish bar. In his 1887 poetry collection Underwoods, Stevenson muses on his having turned from the family profession:

Say not of me that weakly I declined

The labours of my sires, and fled the sea,

The towers we founded and the lamps we lit,

To play at home with paper like a child.

But rather say: In the afternoon of time

A strenuous family dusted from its hands
The sand of granite, and beholding far
Along the sounding coast its pyramids
And tall memorials catch the dying sun,
Smiled well content, and to this childish task
Around the fire addressed its evening hours.

In other respects too, Stevenson was moving away from his upbringing. His dress became more Bohemian; he already wore his hair long, but he now took to wearing a velveteen jacket and rarely attended parties in conventional evening dress. Within the limits of a strict allowance, he visited cheap pubs and brothels. More importantly, he had come to reject Christianity and declared himself an atheist. In January 1873, his father came across the constitution of the LJR (Liberty, Justice, Reverence) Club, of which Stevenson and his cousin Bob were members, which began: "Disregard everything our parents have taught us". Questioning his son about his beliefs, he discovered the truth, leading to a long period of dissension with both parents:

What a damned curse I am to my parents! As my father said "You have rendered my whole life a failure". As my mother said "This is the heaviest affliction that has ever befallen me". O Lord, what a pleasant thing it is to have damned the happiness of (probably) the only two people who care a damn about you in the world.

Early writing and travels

Stevenson was visiting a cousin in England in late 1873 when he met two people who became very important to him: Sidney Colvin and Fanny (Frances Jane) Sitwell. Sitwell was a 34-year-old woman with a son, who was separated from her husband. She attracted the devotion of many who met her, including Colvin, who married her in 1901. Stevenson was also drawn to her, and they kept up a warm correspondence over several years in which he wavered between the role of a suitor and a son (he addressed her as "Madonna"). Colvin became Stevenson's literary adviser and was the first editor of his letters after his death. He placed Stevenson's first paid contribution in The Portfolio, an essay entitled "Roads".

Stevenson was soon active in London literary life, becoming acquainted with many of the writers of the time, including Andrew Lang, Edmund Gosse, and Leslie Stephen, the editor of the Cornhill Magazine who took an interest in Stevenson's work. Stephen took Stevenson to visit a patient at the Edinburgh Infirmary named William Ernest Henley, an energetic and talkative man with a wooden leg. Henley became a close friend and occasional literary collaborator, until a quarrel broke up the friendship in 1888, and he is often considered to be the model for Long John Silver in Treasure Island.

Stevenson was sent to Menton on the French Riviera in November 1873 to recuperate after his health failed. He returned in better health in April 1874 and settled down to his studies, but he returned to France several times after that. He made long and frequent trips to the neighborhood of the Forest of Fontainebleau, staying at Barbizon, Grez-sur-Loing, and Nemours and becoming a member of the artists' colonies there. He also traveled to Paris to visit galleries and the theatres. He qualified for the Scottish bar in July 1875, and his father added a brass plate to the Heriot Row house reading "R.L. Stevenson, Advocate". His law studies did influence his books, but he never practised law; all his energies were spent in travel and writing. One of his journeys was a canoe voyage in Belgium and France with Sir Walter Simpson, a friend from the Speculative Society, a frequent travel companion, and the author of The Art of Golf (1887). This trip was the basis of his first travel book An Inland Voyage (1878).

Marriage

The canoe voyage with Simpson brought Stevenson to Grez in September 1876 where he met Fanny Van de Grift Osbourne (1840–1914), born in Indianapolis. She had married at age 17 and moved to Nevada to rejoin husband Samuel after his participation in the American Civil War. Their children were Isobel (or "Belle"), Lloyd, and Hervey (who died in 1875). But anger over her husband's infidelities led to a number of separations. In 1875, she had taken her children to France where she and Isobel studied art.

Stevenson returned to Britain shortly after this first meeting, but Fanny apparently remained in his thoughts, and he wrote the essay "On falling in love" for the Cornhill Magazine. They met again early in 1877 and became lovers. Stevenson spent much of the following year with her and her children in France. In August 1878, she returned to San Francisco and Stevenson remained in Europe, making the walking trip that formed the basis for Travels with a Donkey in the Cévennes (1879). But he set off to join her in August 1879, against the advice of his friends and without notifying his parents. He took second-class passage on the steamship Devonia, in part to save money but also to learn how others traveled and to increase the adventure of the journey. He then traveled overland by train from New York City to California. He later wrote about the experience in The Amateur Emigrant. It was good experience for his writing, but it broke his health.

He was near death when he arrived in Monterey, California, where some local ranchers nursed him back to health. He stayed for a time at the French Hotel located at 530 Houston Street, now a museum dedicated to his memory called the "Stevenson House". While there, he often dined "on the cuff," as he said, at a nearby restaurant run by Frenchman Jules Simoneau which stood at what is now Simoneau Plaza; several years later, he sent Simoneau an inscribed copy of his novel Strange Case of Dr Jekyll and Mr Hyde (1886), writing that it would be a stranger case still if Robert Louis Stevenson ever forgot Jules Simoneau. While in Monterey, he wrote an evocative article about "the Old Pacific Capital" of Monterey.

By December 1879, Stevenson had recovered his health enough to continue to San Francisco where he struggled "all alone on forty-five cents a day, and sometimes less, with quantities of hard work and many heavy thoughts," in an effort to support himself through his writing. But by the end of the winter, his health was broken again and he found himself at death's door. Fanny was now divorced and recovered from her own illness, and she came to his bedside and nursed him to recovery. "After a while," he wrote, "my spirit got up again in a divine frenzy, and has since kicked and spurred my vile body forward with great emphasis and success." When his father heard of his condition, he cabled him money to help him through this period.

Fanny and Robert were married in May 1880, although he said that he was "a mere complication of cough and bones, much fitter for an emblem of mortality than a bridegroom." He travelled with his new wife and her son Lloyd north of San Francisco to Napa Valley and spent a summer honeymoon at an abandoned mining camp on Mount Saint Helena. He wrote about this experience in The Silverado Squatters. He met Charles Warren Stoddard, co-editor of the Overland Monthly and author of South Sea Idylls, who urged Stevenson to travel to the South Pacific, an idea which returned to him many years later. In August 1880, he sailed with Fanny and Lloyd from New York to Britain and found his parents and his friend Sidney Colvin on the wharf at Liverpool, happy to see him return home. Gradually, his wife was able to patch up differences between father and son and make herself a part of the family through her charm and wit.

Attempted settlement in Europe and the US

Stevenson searched in vain between 1880 and 1887 for a residence suitable to his health. He spent his summers at various places in Scotland and England, including Westbourne, Dorset, a residential area in Bournemouth. It was during his time in Bournemouth that he wrote the story Strange Case of Dr Jekyll and Mr Hyde, naming the character Mr. Poole after the town of Poole which is situated next to Bournemouth. In Westbourne, he named his house Skerryvore after the tallest lighthouse in Scotland, which his uncle Alan had built (1838–44). In the wintertime, Stevenson travelled to France and lived at Davos Platz and the Chalet de Solitude at Hyères, where he was very happy for a time. "I have so many things to make life sweet for me," he wrote, "it seems a pity I cannot have that other one thing—health. But though you will be angry to hear it, I believe, for myself at least, what is is best." In spite of his ill health, he produced the bulk of his best-known work during these years. Treasure Island was published under the pseudonym "Captain George North" and became his first widely popular book; he wrote it during this time, along with Kidnapped, Strange Case of Dr Jekyll and Mr Hyde (which established his wider reputation), The Black Arrow: A Tale of the Two Roses, A Child's Garden of Verses, and Underwoods. He gave a copy of Kidnapped to his friend and frequent Skerryvore visitor Henry James.

His father died in 1887 and Stevenson felt free to follow the advice of his physician to try a complete change of climate, so he headed for Colorado with his mother and family. But after landing in New York, they decided to spend the winter in the Adirondacks at a cure cottage now known as Stevenson Cottage at Saranac Lake, New York. During the intensely cold winter, Stevenson wrote some of his best essays, including Pulvis et Umbra. He also began The Master of Ballantrae and lightheartedly planned a cruise to the southern Pacific Ocean for the following summer.

Politics

Stevenson believed in Conservatism for most of his life. His cousin and biographer Sir Graham Balfour said that "he probably throughout life would, if compelled to vote, have always supported the Conservative candidate." In 1866, Stevenson voted for Benjamin Disraeli, future Conservative Prime Minister of the United Kingdom, over Thomas Carlyle for the Lord Rectorship of the University of Edinburgh. During his college years, he briefly identified himself as a "red-hot socialist". He wrote at age 26: "I look back to the time when I was a Socialist with something like regret…. Now I know that in thus turning Conservative with years, I am going through the normal cycle of change and travelling in the common orbit of men's opinions."

Journey to the Pacific

In June 1888, Stevenson chartered the yacht Casco and set sail with his family from San Francisco. The vessel "plowed her path of snow across the empty deep, far from all track of commerce, far from any hand of help." The sea air and thrill of adventure for a time restored his health, and for nearly three years he wandered the eastern and central Pacific, stopping for extended stays at the Hawaiian Islands where he became a good friend of King Kalākaua. He befriended the king's niece Princess Victoria Kaiulani, who also had Scottish heritage. He spent time at the Gilbert Islands, Tahiti, New Zealand, and the Samoan Islands. During this period, he completed The Master of Ballantrae, composed two ballads based on the legends of the islanders, and wrote The Bottle Imp. He preserved the experience of these years in his various letters and in his In the South Seas (which was published posthumously). He made a voyage in 1889 with Lloyd on the trading schooner Equator, visiting Butaritari, Mariki, Apaiang, and Abemama in the Gilbert Islands. They spent several months on Abemama with tyrant-chief Tem Binoka, whom Stevenson described in In the South Seas.

Stevenson left Sydney on the Janet Nicoll in April 1890 for his third and final voyage among the South Seas islands. He intended to produce another book of travel writing to follow his earlier book In the South Seas, but it was his wife who eventually published her journal of their third voyage. (Fanny misnames the ship in her account The Cruise of the Janet Nichol.) A fellow passenger was Jack Buckland, whose stories of life as an island trader became the inspiration for the character of Tommy Hadden in The Wrecker (1892), which Stevenson and Lloyd Osbourne wrote together. Buckland visited the Stevensons at Vailima in 1894.

Last years

In 1890, Stevenson purchased a tract of about 400 acres (1.6 km^2) in Upolu, an island in Samoa where he established himself on his estate in the village of Vailima after two aborted attempts to visit Scotland. He took the native name Tusitala (Samoan for "Teller of Tales"). His influence spread among the Samoans, who consulted him for advice, and he soon became involved in local politics. He was convinced that the European officials who had been appointed to rule the Samoans were incompetent, and he published A Footnote to History after many futile attempts to resolve the matter. This was such a stinging protest against existing conditions that it resulted in the recall of two officials, and Stevenson feared for a time that it would result in his own deportation. He wrote to Colvin, "I used to think meanly of the plumber; but how he shines beside the politician!"

He also found time to work at his writing, although he felt that "there was never any man had so many irons in the fire". He wrote The Beach of Falesa, Catriona (titled David Balfour in the US), The Ebb-Tide, and the Vailima Letters during this period.

Stevenson grew depressed and wondered if he had exhausted his creative vein, as he had been "overworked bitterly" and that the best he could write was "ditch-water". He even feared that he might again become a helpless invalid. He rebelled against this idea: "I wish to die in my boots; no more Land of Counterpane for me. To be drowned, to be shot, to be thrown from a horse — ay, to be hanged, rather than pass again through that slow dissolution." He then suddenly had a return of energy and he began work on Weir of Hermiston. "It's so good that it frightens me," he is reported to have exclaimed. He felt that this was the best work he had done.

On 3 December 1894, Stevenson was talking to his wife and straining to open a bottle of wine when he suddenly exclaimed, "What's that?", asked his wife "does my face look strange?", and collapsed. He died within a few hours, probably of a cerebral haemorrhage. He was 44 years old. The Samoans insisted on surrounding his body with a watch-guard during the night and on bearing him on their shoulders to nearby Mount Vaea, where they buried him on a spot overlooking the sea on land donated by British Acting Vice Consul Thomas Trood. Stevenson had always wanted his Requiem inscribed on his tomb:

Under the wide and starry sky,

Dig the grave and let me lie.

Glad did I live and gladly die,

And I laid me down with a will.

This be the verse you grave for me:

Here he lies where he longed to be;

Home is the sailor, home from sea,

And the hunter home from the hill.

Stevenson was loved by the Samoans, and his tombstone epigraph was translated to a Samoan song of grief. (Source: Wikipedia)

CPSIA information can be obtained
at www.ICGtesting.com
Printed in the USA
LVHW090849230620
658719LV00003B/518

9 789390 171347